Adam and Eve in the Garden of Eden

Coloring & Activity Book for Kids

Learn Color Grow in Faith!

Fun Activities Inside!

The Lord God planted a garden
in Eden, in the east; and there
He put the man He had formed.

Genesis 2:8

1. God Creates Adam

2. Adam in the Beautiful Garden

3. Adam Naming the Animals

4. God's Beautiful Creation: Eve

5. Adam and Eve Exploring Eden

6. Animals Living Peacefully

7. The Tree in the Garden

8. Caring for the Garden

9. Adam and Eve Thanking God

10. Garden Full of Creation

11. Family Activity

Adam and Eve enjoyed God's garden together with the animals.

☆ Help Adam and Eve walk along the path and enjoy God's beautiful creation! ☆

Count how many of each animal and bird you see in the garden.

Rabbits	Squirrels	Birds	Butterflies	Sheep	Ducks	Fish	Lions

12. God's
Beautiful Garden
God saw everything He had made,
and it was very good.
Genesis 1:31

Made in United States
Orlando, FL
06 November 2026

90230153R00017